PIANO VOCAL GUITAR

ESSENTIAL SONGS

The 1970s

CW00741857

HLE
Hal Leonard Europe
Distributed by Music Sales

Exclusive Distributors:
Music Sales Limited
8/9 Frith Street, London W1D 3JB, UK.

Order No. HLE90002748
ISBN 1-84609-360-0
This book © Copyright 2006 by Hal Leonard Europe

Printed in the USA

Your Guarantee of Quality
As publishers, we strive to produce every book to the highest commercial standards.
The book has been carefully designed to minimise awkward page turns and to make
playing from it a real pleasure.
Throughout, the printing and binding have been planned to ensure a sturdy, attractive
publication which should give years of enjoyment.
If your copy fails to meet our high standards, please inform us and we will gladly
replace it.

www.musicsales.com

CONTENTS

AFTERNOON DELIGHT

Words and Music by
BILL DANOFF

10

BABY, I LOVE YOUR WAY

Words and Music by
PETER FRAMPTON

Shad-ows grow __ so long __ be-fore my
Moon ap-pears __ to shine __ and light the
I can see __ the sun-set __ in your

eyes __ and they're mov-ing
sky __ with the help __
eyes, __ brown and grey __

a-
of some
and

cross the page. __ Sud-den-ly __ the day __ turns in-to night __
fire-fly. __ Won-der how __ they have __ the pow'r to shine. __
blue be-sides. __ Clouds are stalk-ing is-lands in the sun. __

THE AIR THAT I BREATHE

Words and Music by ALBERT HAMMOND
and MICHAEL HAZELWOOD

AMERICAN PIE

Words and Music by
DON McLEAN

A long, long time a-go I can still re-mem-ber how that

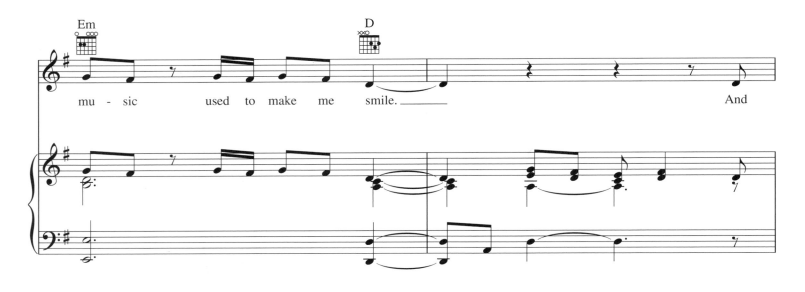

mu-sic used to make me smile. And

I knew if I had my chance that I could make those peo-ple dance and

day the mu - sic died. And they were sing - in'

this - 'll be the day ____ that I ____ die. ____

Additional Lyrics

2. Now for ten years we've been on our own,
And moss grows fat on a rollin' stone
But that's not how it used to be
When the jester sang for the king and queen
In a coat he borrowed from James Dean
And a voice that came from you and me
Oh and while the king was looking down,
The jester stole his thorny crown
The courtroom was adjourned,
No verdict was returned
And while Lenin read a book on Marx
The quartet practiced in the park
And we sang dirges in the dark
The day the music died
We were singin'...bye-bye... etc.

3. Helter-skelter in the summer swelter
The birds flew off with a fallout shelter
Eight miles high and fallin' fast,
It landed foul on the grass
The players tried for a forward pass,
With the jester on the sidelines in a cast
Now the half-time air was sweet perfume
While the sergeants played a marching tune
We all got up to dance
But we never got the chance
'Cause the players tried to take the field,
The marching band refused to yield
Do you recall what was revealed
The day the music died
We started singin'... bye-bye...etc.

4. And there we were all in one place,
A generation lost in space
With no time left to start again
So come on, Jack be nimble, Jack be quick,
Jack Flash sat on a candlestick
'Cause fire is the devil's only friend
And as I watched him on the stage
My hands were clenched in fits of rage
No angel born in hell
Could break that Satan's spell
And as the flames climbed high into the night
To light the sacrificial rite
I saw Satan laughing with delight
The day the music died
He was singin'...bye-bye...etc.

BABY COME BACK

Words and Music by JOHN C. CROWLEY
and PETER BECKETT

34

BAD CASE OF LOVIN' YOU
(Doctor, Doctor)

Words and Music by
JOHN MOON MARTIN

Driving Rock

Whoa.

The hot sum-mer night

fell like a net.
don't make no pret-ty heart;
by twen-ty-one to zip,

I've got-ta
I learned
Smile of

Tell me ma - ma, are you gon-na stop? _

You had me down _

bad case of

lov - in' you. _____

BEST OF MY LOVE

Words and Music by JOHN DAVID SOUTHER,
DON HENLEY and GLENN FREY

Moderately slow

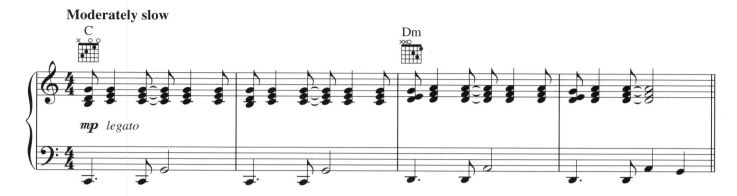

Ev-er-y night ___ I'm ly-in' in bed, ___ hold-in' you close ___ in my
Beau-ti-ful fac-es and loud emp-ty plac-es, look at the way that we

dreams; ___ think-in' a-bout ___ all the things that we ___ said ___ and
live; ___ wast-in' our time ___ on cheap talk and wine

BAD GIRLS

Words and Music by JOE "BEANS" ESPOSITO,
EDWARD HOKENSON, BRUCE SUDANO
and DONNA SUMMER

BAKER STREET

Words and Music by
GERRY RAFFERTY

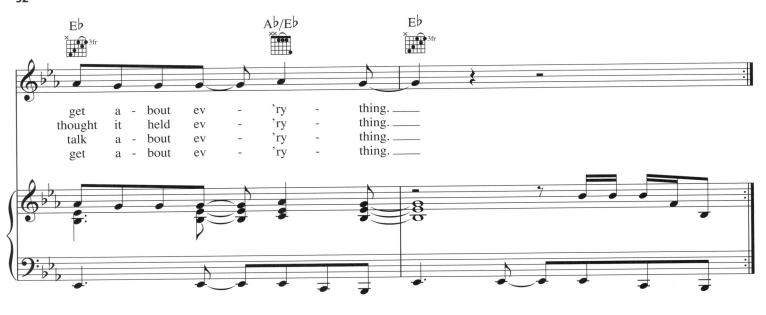

get a - bout ev - 'ry - thing. _____
thought it held ev - 'ry - thing. _____
talk a - bout ev - 'ry - thing. _____
get a - bout ev - 'ry - thing. _____

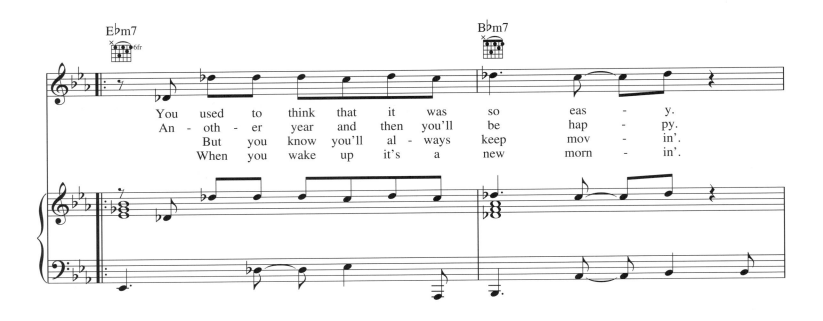

You used to think that it was so eas - y.
An - oth - er year and then you'll be hap - py.
But you know you'll al - ways keep mov - in'.
When you wake up it's a new morn - in'.

You used to see that it was so eas - y. But
Just one more year and then you'll be hap - py. But
You know he's nev - er gon - na stop mov - in'. 'Cause
The sun is shin - in', it's a new morn - in' and

you're try – in', you're try – in' now. ____
you're cry – in', you're cry – in' now. ____
he's roll – in', he's the roll – in' stone. ____
you're go – in', you're go – in' home. ____

1st time: D.S. (with repeats)
2nd time: Repeat and Fade

BAND ON THE RUN

Words and Music by
PAUL and LINDA McCARTNEY

Brighter beat

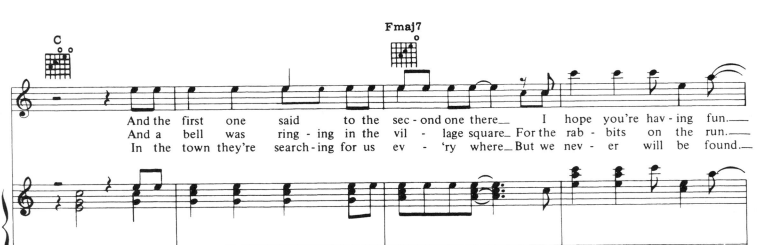

BEST THING THAT EVER HAPPENED TO ME

Words and Music by
JIM WEATHERLY

BILLY, DON'T BE A HERO

Words and Music by PETER CALLENDER
and MITCH MURRAY

I heard she threw that let-ter _____ a - way. _____

Repeat and Fade

BOOGIE NIGHTS

Words and Music by
ROD TEMPERTON

keep on danc - ing. Got to keep on danc - ing, keep on danc - ing.

Em13

(Boo - gie ___ night, ___ whoa, ___
(Do you wan-na boo-gie? Boo - gie, boo - gie, boo - gie

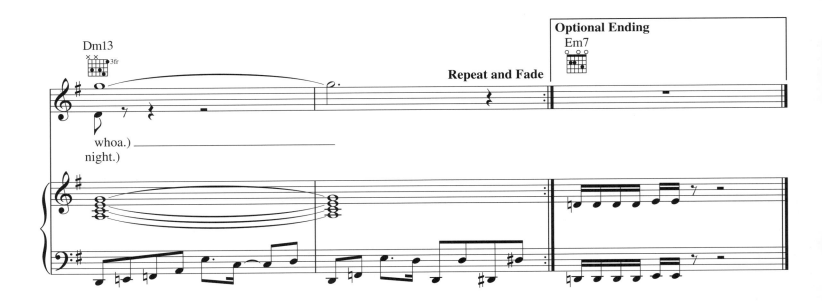

Dm13

Repeat and Fade

Optional Ending
Em7

whoa.) ___
night.)

BURNING LOVE

Words and Music by
DENNIS LINDE

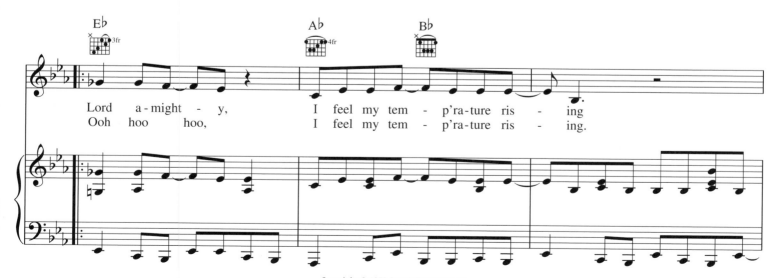

Lord a-might-y, I feel my tem-p'ra-ture ris-ing
Ooh hoo hoo, I feel my tem-p'ra-ture ris-ing.

THE BOYS ARE BACK IN TOWN

Words and Music by
PHILIP PARRIS LYNOTT

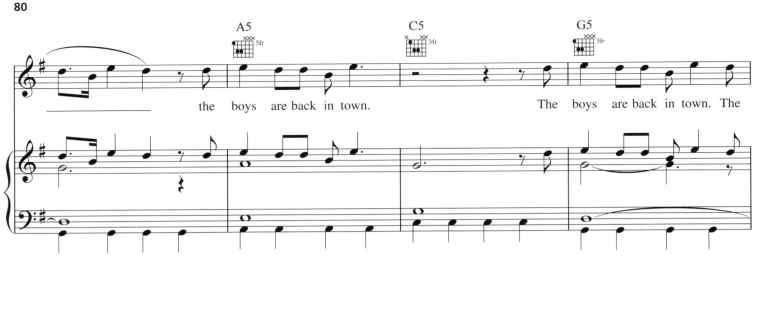

the boys are back in town. The boys are back in town. The

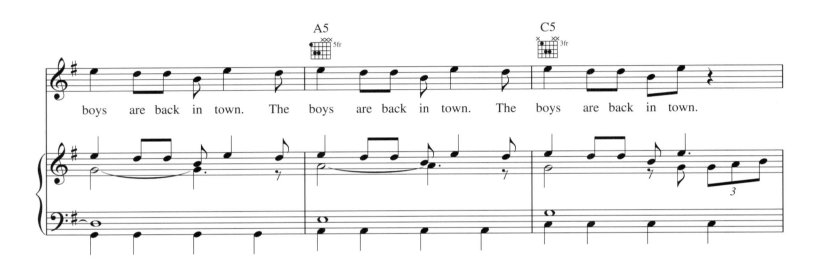

boys are back in town. The boys are back in town. The boys are back in town.

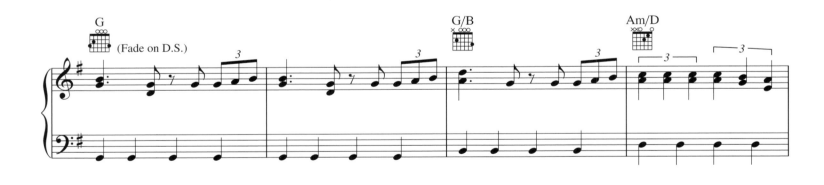

(Fade on D.S.)

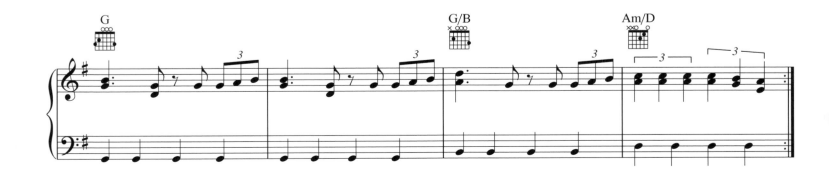

Interlude

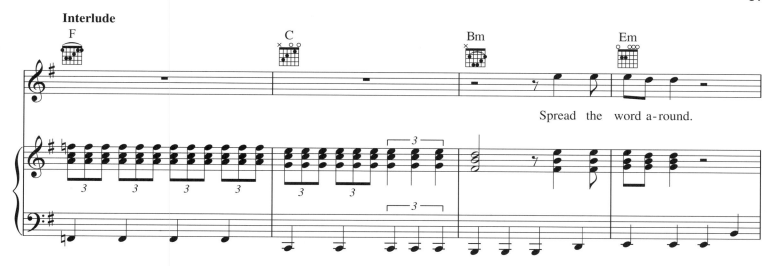

Spread the word a-round.

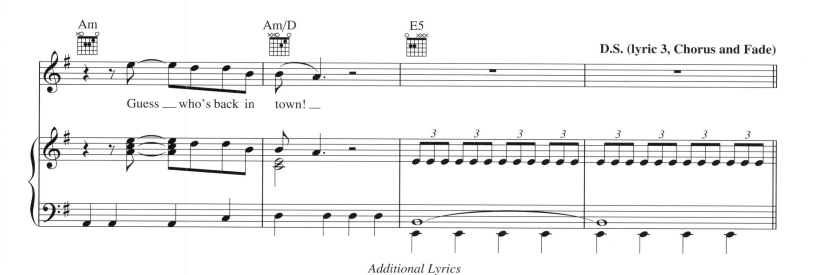

D.S. (lyric 3, Chorus and Fade)

Guess _ who's back in town! _

Additional Lyrics

2. You know that chick that used to dance a lot
   Every night she'd be on the floor shaking what she'd got
   Man, when I tell you she was cool, she was hot
   I mean she was steaming.

   And that time over at Johnny's place
   Well, this chick got up and she slapped Johnny's face
   Man, we just fell about the place
   If that chick don't wanna know, forget her.

   (Chorus & Interlude)

3. Friday night they'll be dressed to kill
   Down at Dino's Bar and Grill
   The drink will flow and blood will spill
   And if the boys want to fight, you better let 'em.

   That jukebox in the corner blasting out my favorite song
   The nights are getting warmer, it won't be long
   It won't be long till summer comes
   Now that the boys are here again.

   (Chorus and Fade)

CAN'T SMILE WITHOUT YOU

Words and Music by CHRIS ARNOLD,
DAVID MARTIN and GEOFF MORROW

CAR WASH

Words and Music by
NORMAN WHITFIELD

Moderately slow (with a double time feel)

Clap hands

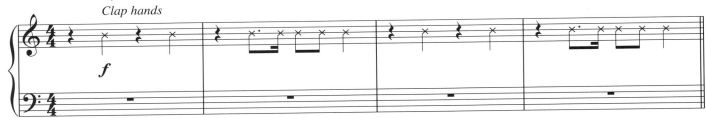

Woo _____   You might not ev - er get

rich   but let me tell ya it's bet - ter than dig - gin' a ditch. _

94

chines _____ hum - min'. Let me tell you it's al - ways

cool, and the boss don't mind some - times if you

act a fool at the car wash. _____

Repeat and Fade

{ Work - in' at the }
{ Talk - in' a - bout the } car wash, _ yeah! _

CLAIR

Words and Music by
GILBERT O'SULLIVAN

(They Long To Be)
CLOSE TO YOU

Lyric by HAL DAVID
Music by BURT BACHARACH

COME AND GET IT

Words and Music by
PAUL McCARTNEY

THE CLOSER I GET TO YOU

Words and Music by JAMES MTUME
and REGGIE LUCAS

COME SAIL AWAY

Words and Music by
DENNIS DeYOUNG

CRACKLIN' ROSIE

Words and Music by
NEIL DIAMOND

DANCING QUEEN

Words and Music by BENNY ANDERSSON,
BJORN ULVAEUS and STIG ANDERSON

DANIEL

Words and Music by ELTON JOHN
and BERNIE TAUPIN

Moderately fast

Dan - iel is trav -
They say Spain is pret -
Instrumental

- 'ling to - night ___ on a plane. ___
- ty, ___ 'though I've nev - er been. ___

DREAMS

Words and Music by
STEVIE NICKS

Moderately, with a beat

Now, here you go _____ a - gain. _ You say
Now, here I go _____ a - gain. _ I see

you want _ your free - dom.
the crys - tal vi - sions.

Well, who am I _
I keep my vi -

_____ to keep _ you down?
- sions to _____ my - self.

DON'T GIVE UP ON US

Words and Music by
TONY MACAULAY

DREAM WEAVER

Words and Music by
GARY WRIGHT

Moderately fast

I've just closed my
Fly me high through the
Though me the dawn may be

eyes ___ a - gain, ___ climbed a - board the dream ___
star - ry skies, ___ or may - be to ___
com - ing soon, ___ there still may ___

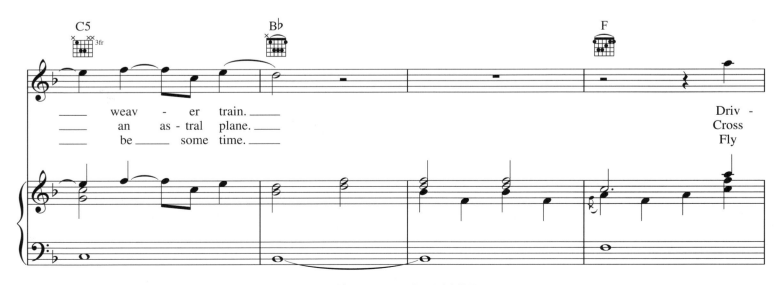

___ weav - er train. ___ Driv-
___ an as - tral plane. ___ Cross
___ be ___ some time. ___ Fly

DRIFT AWAY

Words and Music by
MENTOR WILLIAMS

FAME

Words and Music by JOHN LENNON,
DAVID BOWIE and CARLOS ALOMAR

EVERYTHING IS BEAUTIFUL

Words and Music by
RAY STEVENS

2. We shouldn't care about the length of his hair or the color of his skin,
   Don't worry about what shows from without but the love that lives within,
   We gonna get it all together now and everything gonna work out fine,
   Just take a little time to look on the good side my friend and straighten it out in your mind.

FEELINGS
(¿Dime?)

English Words and Music by MORRIS ALBERT
and LOUIS GASTE
Spanish Words by THOMAS FUNDORA

Moderately slow

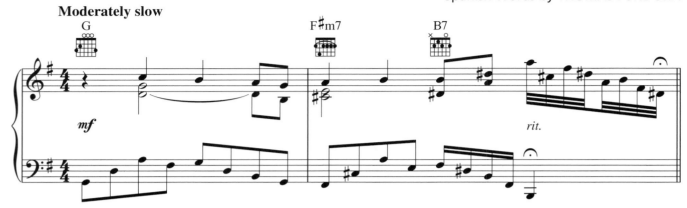

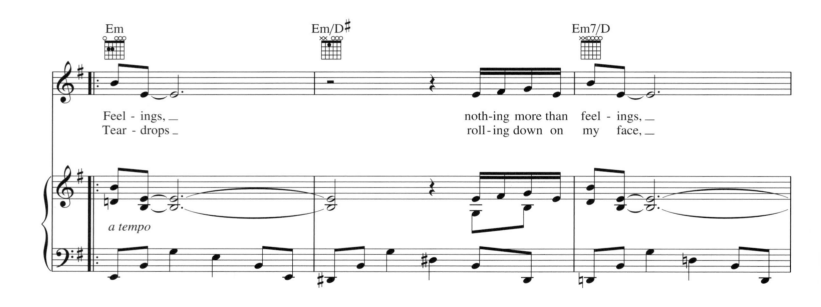

Feel - ings, ___ noth-ing more than feel - ings, ___
Tear - drops ___ roll-ing down on my face, ___

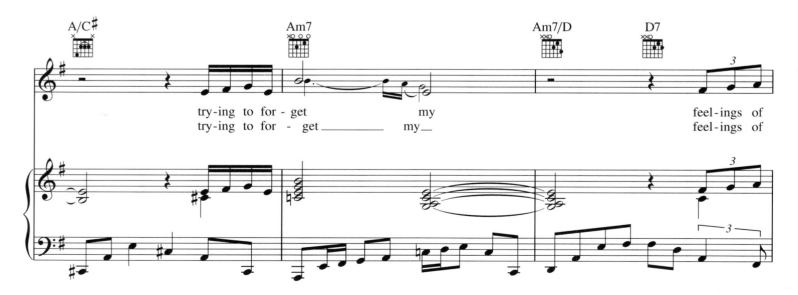

try-ing to for - get my feel-ings of
try-ing to for - get ___ my ___ feel-ings of

you'll nev-er come a-gain.
a-gain in my
you'll nev-er come a-

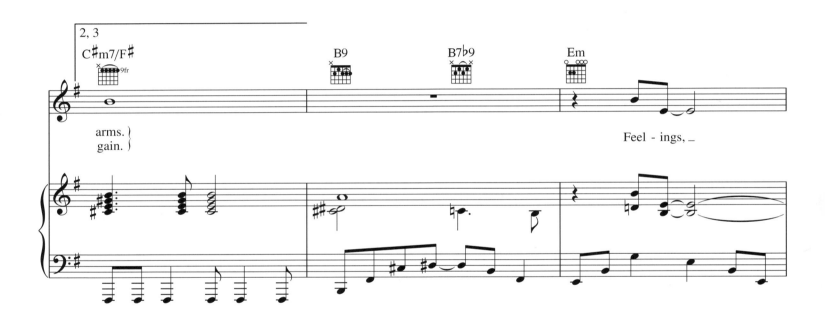

arms.
gain.

Feel-ings, __

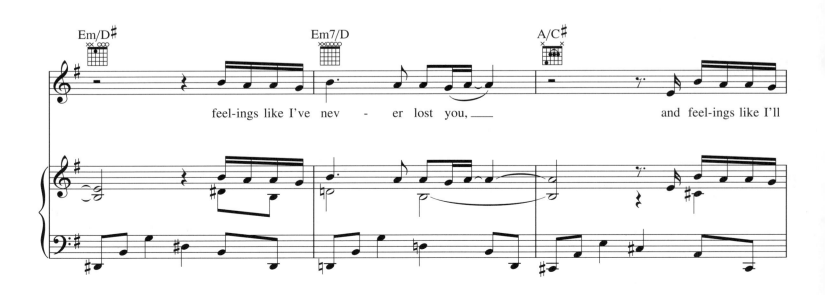

feel-ings like I've nev-er lost you, ___ and feel-ings like I'll

THE FIRST CUT IS THE DEEPEST

Words and Music by
CAT STEVENS

FLY LIKE AN EAGLE

Words and Music by
STEVE MILLER

Tick, tock, _ tick. Doot, doot, do, do.

Time keeps on slip-pin', slip-pin', slip-pin' _____ in-to the fu-

-ture. _____

Play 4 times

GARDEN PARTY

Words and Music by
RICK NELSON

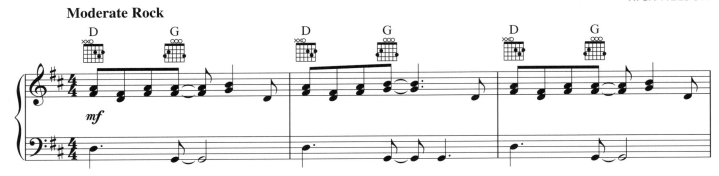

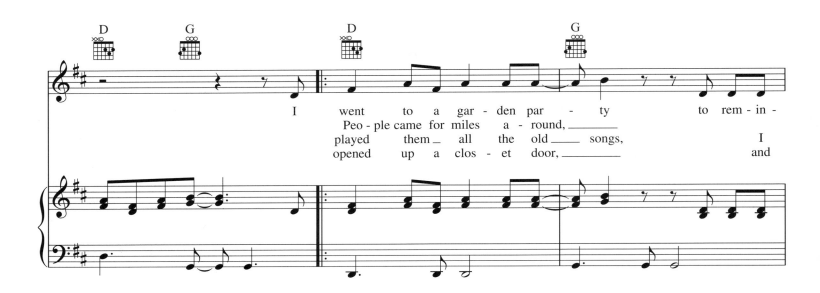

I went to a gar-den par-ty to rem-in-
Peo-ple came for miles a-round, I
played them all the old songs, and
opened up a clos-et door,

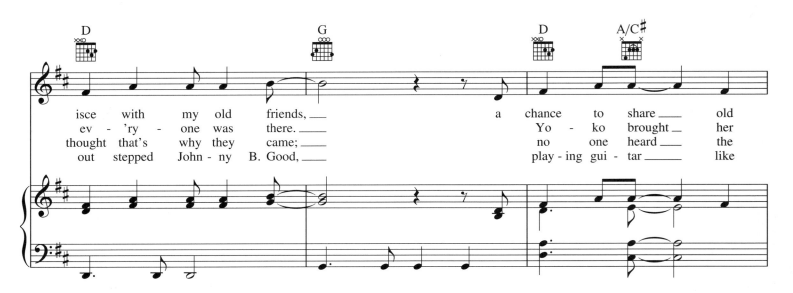

isce with my old friends, a chance to share old
ev-'ry-one was there. Yo-ko brought her
thought that's why they came; no one heard the
out stepped John-ny B. Good, play-ing gui-tar like

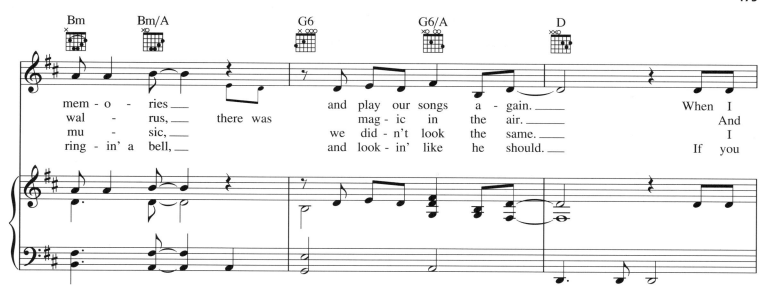

mem - o - ries ___ and play our songs a - gain. ___ When I
wal - rus, ___ there was magic in the air. ___ And
mu - sic, ___ we did - n't look the same. ___ I
ring - in' a bell, ___ and look - in' like he should. ___ If you

got to the gar - den par - ty, they all knew ___ my name, ___
o - ver ___ in the cor - ner, much to my ___ sur - prise, ___
said hel - lo to "Mar - y Lou," she be - longs ___ to me. ___
got - ta play at gar - den par - ties, I wish you a lot of luck, ___

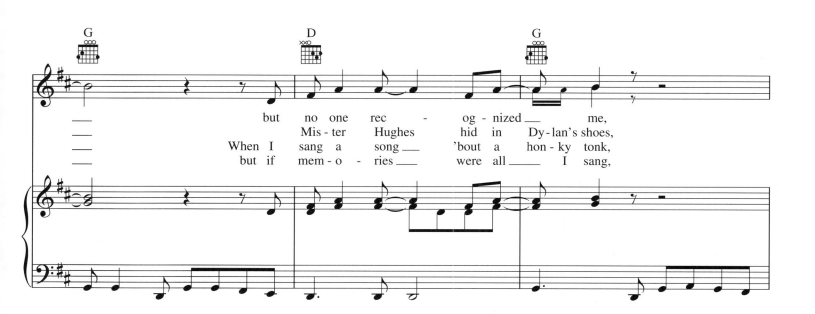

___ but no one rec - og - nized ___ me,
___ Mis - ter Hughes hid in Dy - lan's shoes,
___ When I sang a song ___ 'bout a hon - ky tonk,
___ but if mem - o - ries ___ were all ___ I sang,

GYPSYS, TRAMPS AND THIEVES

Words and Music by
ROBERT STONE

(Hey There)
LONELY GIRL

Words and Music by EARL SHUMAN
and LEON CARR

(Hey, Won't You Play)
ANOTHER SOMEBODY DONE SOMEBODY WRONG SONG

Words and Music by LARRY BUTLER
and CHIPS MOMAN

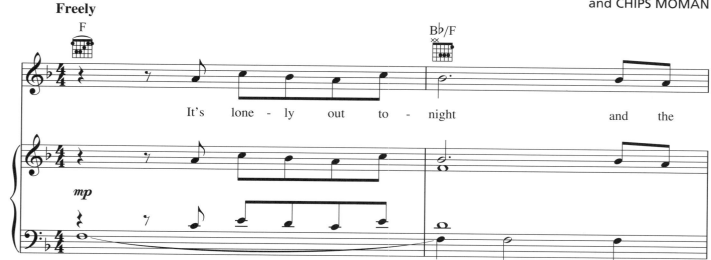

It's lone-ly out to-night and the

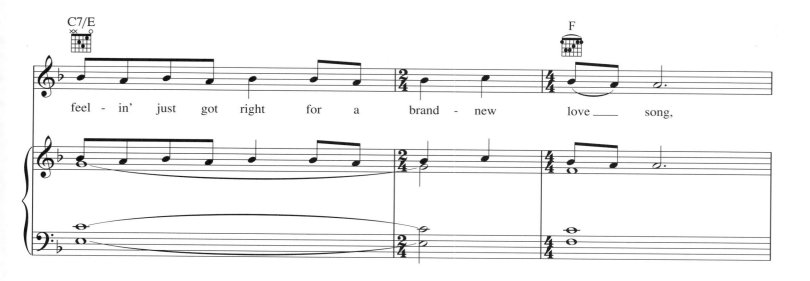

feel-in' just got right for a brand-new love ___ song,

some-bod-y done some-bod-y wrong song.

HONKY CAT

Words and Music by ELTON JOHN
and BERNIE TAUPIN

Brightly, with spirit

When __ I look back, boy, I must __ have been green, __ bop-pin' in the coun-try,

HOW LONG

Words and Music by
PAUL CARRACK

Lyrics:
How long _____ has this been go - ing on?

HURTING EACH OTHER

Words by PETER UDELL
Music by GARY GELD

(I Never Promised You A)
ROSE GARDEN

Words and Music by
JOE SOUTH

go, oh, oh, oh. ____ I beg your par-don,

I nev-er prom-ised you a rose ____ gar - den.

1. I could
2.
3. I could
4.

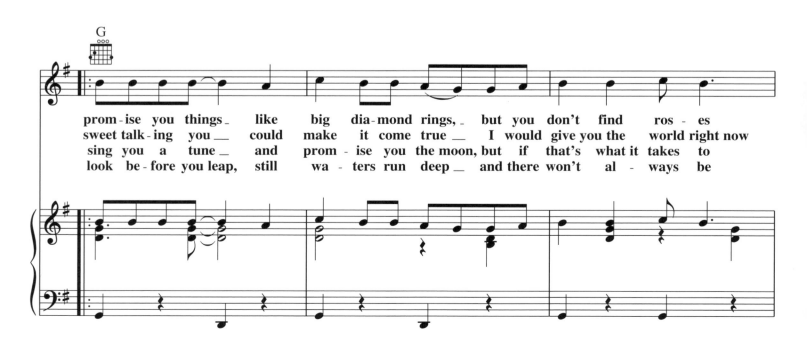

prom-ise you things__ like big dia-mond rings, but you don't find ros - es
sweet talk-ing you__ could make it come true__ I would give you the world right now
sing you a tune__ and prom-ise you the moon, but if that's what it takes to
look be-fore you leap, still wa-ters run deep__ and there won't al - ways be

I WILL SURVIVE

Words and Music by DINO FEKARIS
and FREDERICK J. PERREN

IF YOU LEAVE ME NOW

Words and Music by
PETER CETERA

Ooh, _____ girl, _____ just
Ooh, ma - ma, _____ I just

got to have _ you by my side. _____
got to have _ your lov - in'. _____

Repeat and Fade

Ooh, _____

I'LL TAKE YOU THERE

Words and Music by
ALVERTIS ISBELL

Come on now. Play on it, play on it.

Ba - by, lit - tle ba - by,

IT NEVER RAINS
(In Southern California)

Words and Music by ALBERT HAMMOND
and MICHAEL HAZELWOOD

KILLING ME SOFTLY WITH HIS SONG

Words by NORMAN GIMBEL
Music by CHARLES FOX

Strum-ming my pain with his fin - gers,

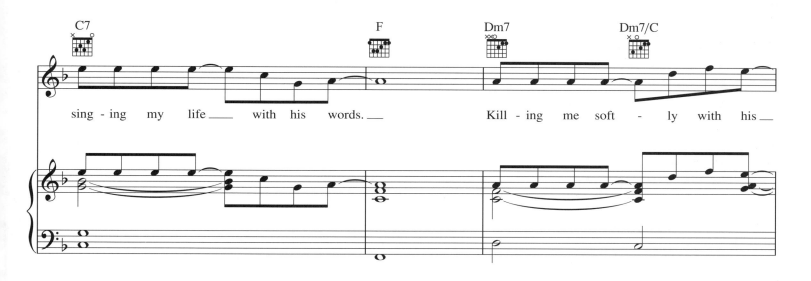

sing-ing my life with his words. Kill-ing me soft - ly with his

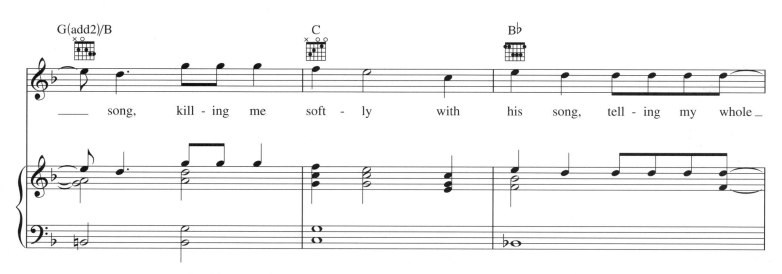

song, kill-ing me soft-ly with his song, tell-ing my whole

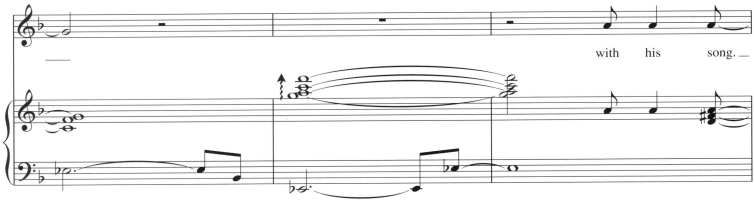

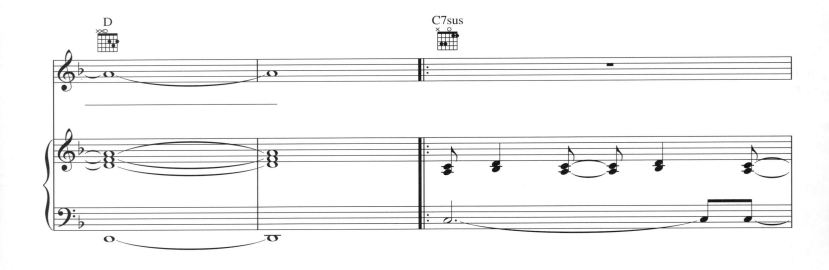

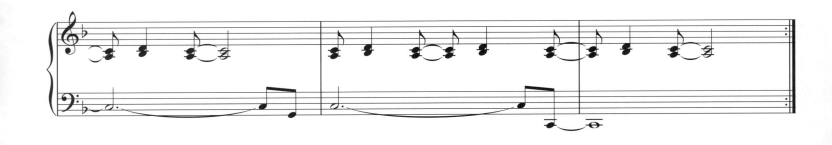

IT'S SO EASY
from THE BUDDY HOLLY STORY

Words and Music by BUDDY HOLLY
and NORMAN PETTY

JOY TO THE WORLD

Words and Music by
HOYT AXTON

KNOCK THREE TIMES

Words and Music by IRWIN LEVINE
and L. RUSSELL BROWN

LAY DOWN SALLY

Words and Music by ERIC CLAPTON,
MARCY LEVY and GEORGE TERRY

There is noth-ing that ___ is wrong ___ in want-ing you ___ to stay ___
sun ain't near-ly on ___ the rise, ___ and we still got ___ the moon ___
long to see ___ the morn-ing light ___ col-or-ing ___ your face ___

___ here ___ with me.   I
___ and stars ___ a - bove.
___ so dream - i - ly.   So

LET IT BE

Words and Music by JOHN LENNON
and PAUL McCARTNEY

When I find my-self __ in times of trou-ble

Instrumental

Moth-er Mar - y comes to me speak-ing words of wis - dom; let it

be. ___ And in my hour of dark - ness, she is

THE LOGICAL SONG

Words and Music by RICK DAVIES
and ROGER HODGSON

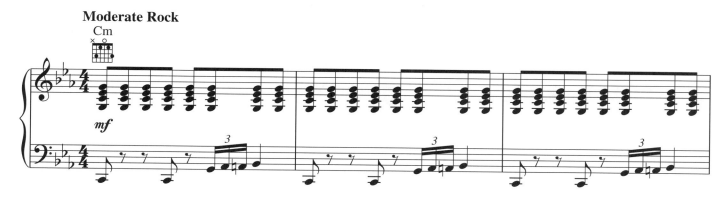

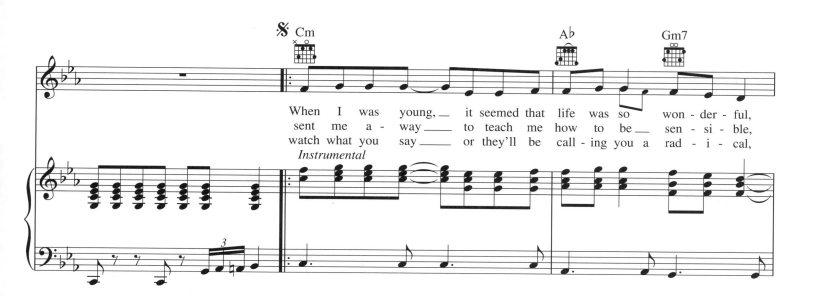

When I was young, __ it seemed that life was so won-der-ful,
sent me a-way __ to teach me how to be __ sen-si-ble,
watch what you say __ or they'll be call-ing you a rad-i-cal,

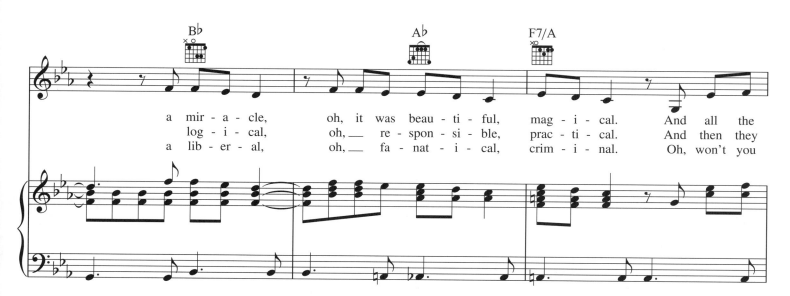

a mir-a-cle, oh, it was beau-ti-ful, mag-i-cal. And all the
log-i-cal, oh, __ re-spon-si-ble, prac-ti-cal. And then they
a lib-er-al, oh, __ fa-nat-i-cal, crim-i-nal. Oh, won't you

birds in the trees,___ well, they'd be sing-ing so hap-pi-ly, oh, joy-ful-ly,
showed me a world___ where I could be so de-pend-a-ble, oh, clin-i-cal,
sign up your name;___ we'd like to feel you're ac-cept-a-ble, re-spect-a-ble,

oh, play-ful-ly watch-ing me.
oh, in-tel-lec-tu-al, cyn-i-cal.
oh,___ pre-sent-a-ble. A veg-'ta-ble!

1, 3

But then they

2, 4

Instrumental ends There are times___ }
But at night,___ }

when all___ the world's___ a-sleep,___

LET'S STAY TOGETHER

Words and Music by AL GREEN,
WILLIE MITCHELL and AL JACKSON, JR.

THE LONG AND WINDING ROAD

Words and Music by JOHN LENNON
and PAUL McCARTNEY

The long and wind-ing road, _____ that _____ leads _____
wild and wind-y night _____ that the _____ rain _____

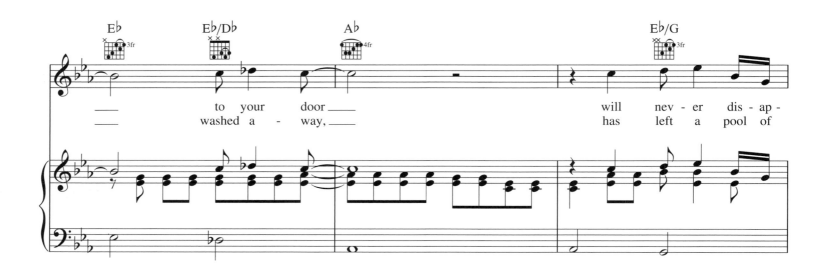

_____ to your door _____ will nev-er dis-ap-
_____ washed a-way, _____ has left a pool of

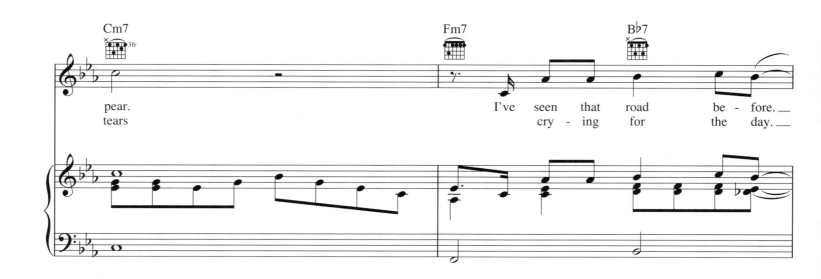

pear. I've seen that road be-fore. _____
tears cry-ing for the day. _____

LOOKS LIKE WE MADE IT

Words and Music by RICHARD KERR
and WILL JENNINGS

ME AND YOU AND A DOG NAMED BOO

Words and Music by
LOBO

MORNING HAS BROKEN

Musical Arrangement by CAT STEVENS
Words by ELEANOR FARJEON

Morn - ing has brok - en like the first morn -
Sweet the rain's new fall, sun - lit from heav -

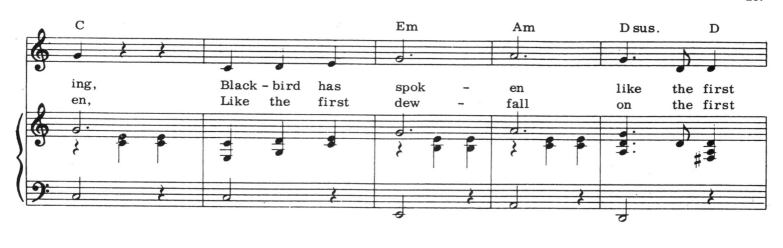

ing,   Black - bird has spok — en   like the first
en,   Like the first dew — fall   on the first

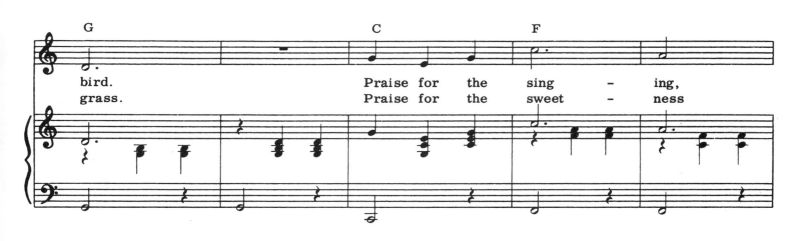

bird.   Praise for the sing — ing,
grass.   Praise for the sweet — ness

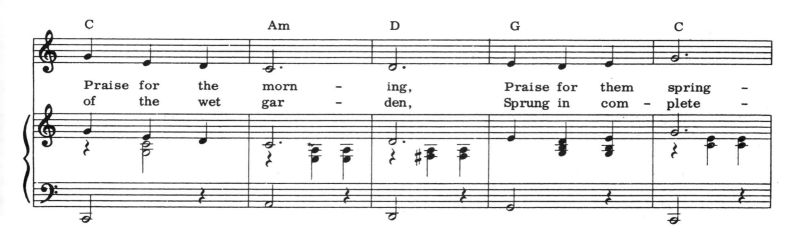

Praise for the morn — ing, Praise for them spring —
of the wet gar — den, Sprung in com — plete —

ing   fresh from___ the world.
ness   where his___ feet pass.

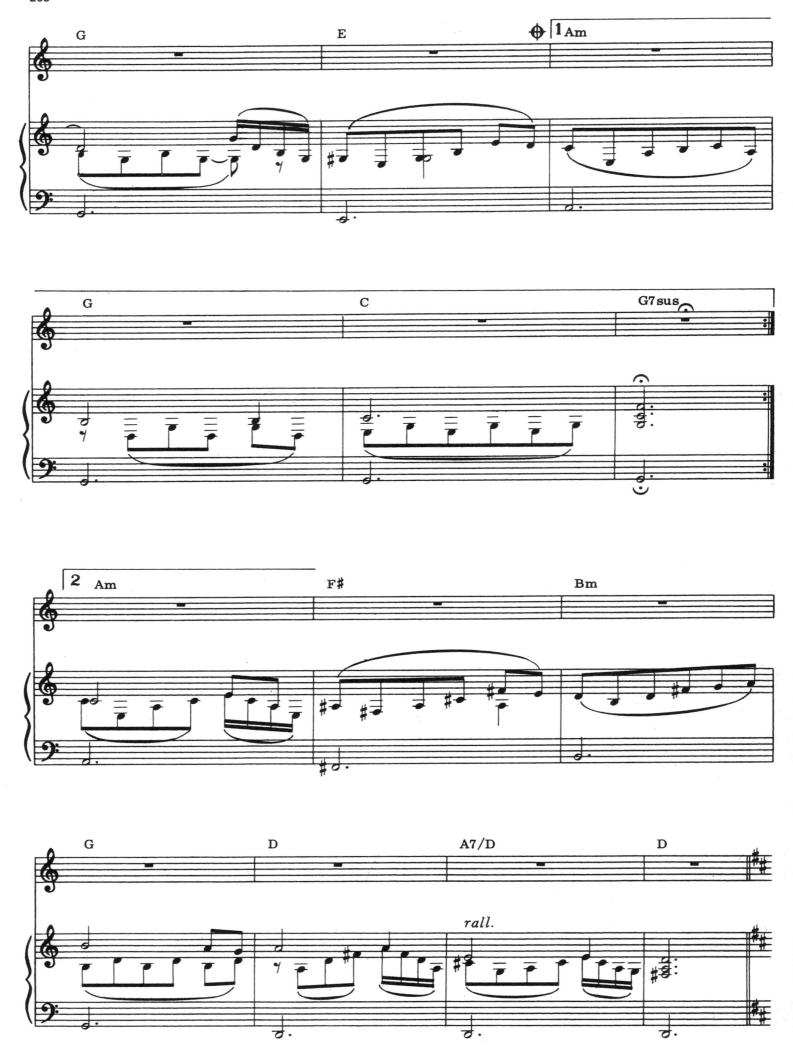

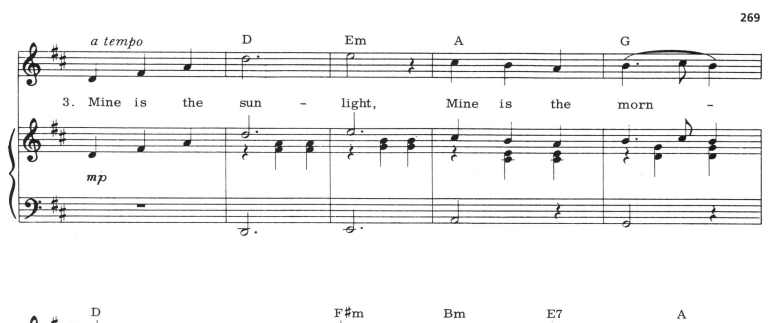

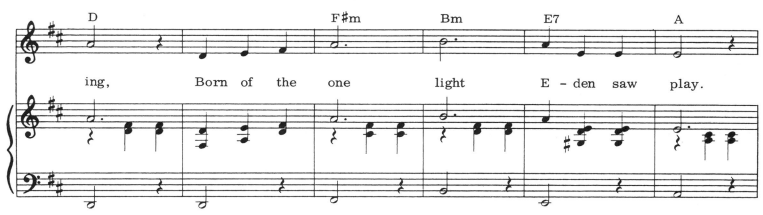

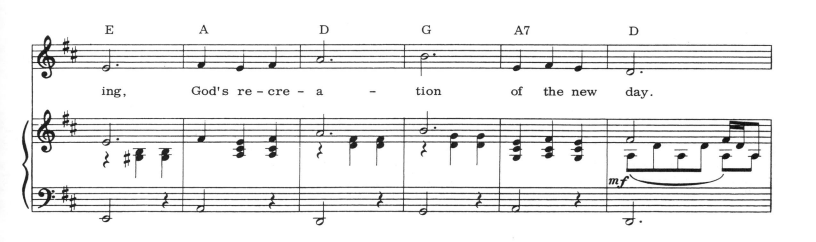

MY LOVE

Words and Music by
PAUL and LINDA McCARTNEY

1. And when I go a-way, __ I know my heart can stay __ with my
2. And when the cup-board's bare, __ I'll still find some-thing there __ with my
3. Don't ev-er ask me why __ I nev-er said good-bye __ to my

love. It's un-der-stood, __ it's in the hands __ of my love, _____
love. It's un-der-stood, __ it's in the hands __ of my love, _____ And
love. It's un-der-stood, __ it's in the hands __ of my love, _____

my love does it good, Wo-wo wo-wo, wo-wo

MY SWEET LORD

Words and Music by
GEORGE HARRISON

NOTHING FROM NOTHING

Words and Music by BILLY PRESTON
and BRUCE FISHER

Energetically, in 2

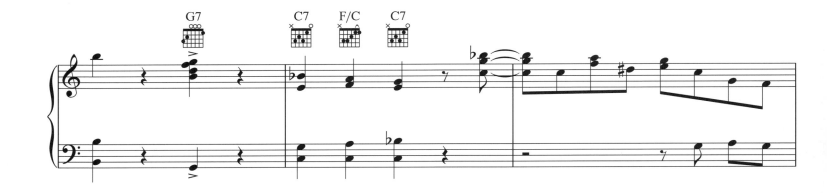

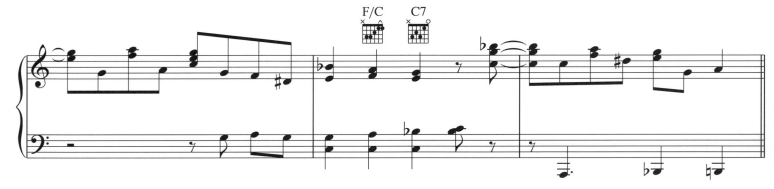

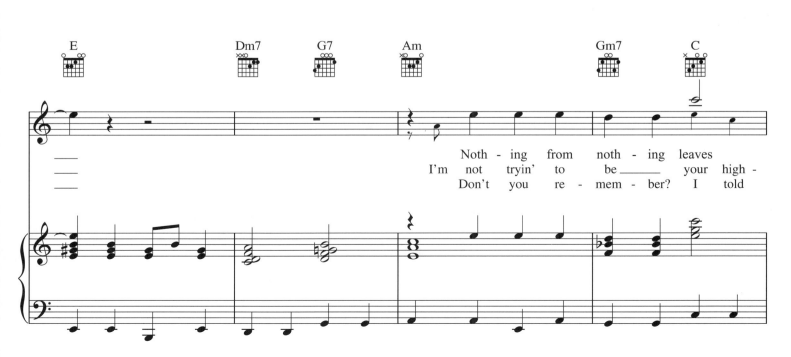

PEG

Words and Music by WALTER BECKER
and DONALD FAGEN

POETRY MAN

Words and Music by
PHOEBE SNOW

Talk ___ to me some more. ___ You don't have to go. ___ You're the

po - et - ry man ___ and you make ___ things all ___ right.

RAINDROPS KEEP FALLIN' ON MY HEAD

from BUTCH CASSIDY AND THE SUNDANCE KID

Lyric by HAL DAVID
Music by BURT BACHARACH

Rain - drops keep fall - in' on my head, and just like the guy whose feet are too big for his bed, noth - in' seems to fit. Those rain - drops are fall - in' on my head. They keep fall - in' so I just did me some talk - in' to the

PRECIOUS AND FEW

Words and Music by
WALTER D. NIMS

REUNITED

Words and Music by DINO FEKARIS
and FREDDIE PERREN

one per-fect fit ___ and, sug - ar, this one is it. ___ We both are so ex - cit - ed, 'cause we're

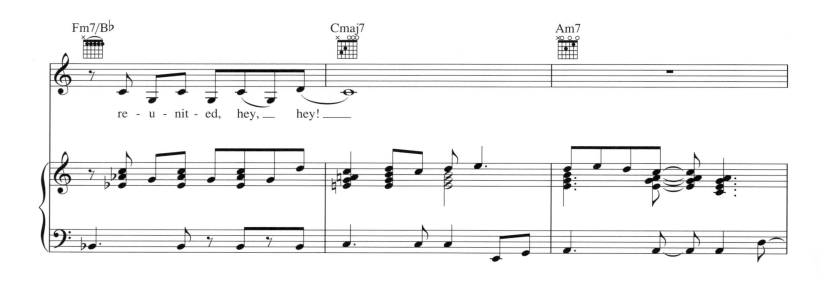

re - u - nit - ed, hey, ___ hey! ___

Additional Lyrics

4. Ooh, listen, baby, I won't ever make you cry, I won't let one day go by
   Without holding you, without kissing you, without loving you.
   Ooh, you're my everything, only you know how to free
   All the love there is in me.
   I wanna let you know, I won't let you go.
   I wanna let you know, I won't let you go.
   Ooh, feels so good!

SHAMBALA

Words and Music by
DANIEL MOORE

my trou - bles, wash a - way___ my pain with___ the
is help - ful, ev - 'ry - one___ is kind on___ the
my sis - ter by the flow - ers in her eyes on___ the

RIKKI DON'T LOSE THAT NUMBER

Words and Music by WALTER BECKER
and DONALD FAGEN

SILLY LOVE SONGS

Words and Music by
PAUL and LINDA McCARTNEY

Moderately Bright

You'd think that peo - ple would have had e - nough of Sil - ly Love___ Songs.___

But I look a - round me and I see___ it is - n't so.

Some peo - ple wan - na fill the world___ with Sil - ly Love Songs,___

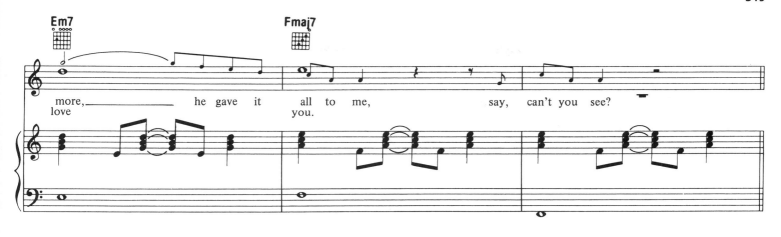

more,⎯⎯⎯⎯ he gave it all to me, say, can't you see?
love you.

I⎯⎯ I⎯⎯ can't ex - plain,⎯⎯ the feel-ing's plain to me, say, can't you see?
How⎯⎯⎯⎯ can I tell⎯⎯ you a - bout⎯⎯ my⎯ loved one?

I love you.

Ah,⎯⎯⎯ How⎯⎯⎯⎯ he gave me more,⎯⎯⎯ he gave it all to me, say, can't you see?
How⎯⎯⎯⎯ can I tell⎯⎯ you a - bout⎯⎯ my⎯ loved one?

I love you.

SONG SUNG BLUE

Words and Music by
NEIL DIAMOND

and be-fore you know it start to feel-in' good. ___ You sim-ply got no choice. _

Fun - ny thing, ___ but you can sing ___ it with a

cry in your voice ___ and be-fore you know it start to feel-in' good. ___

You sim - ply got no choice.

D.S. al Coda

CODA

STAYIN' ALIVE

from the Motion Picture SATURDAY NIGHT FEVER

Words and Music by ROBIN GIBB,
MAURICE GIBB and BARRY GIBB

TAKE ME HOME, COUNTRY ROADS

Words and Music by JOHN DENVER,
BILL DANOFF and TAFFY NIVERT

SUMMER BREEZE

Words and Music by JAMES SEALS
and DASH CROFTS

See the cur-tains hang-in' in the win-dow ____ in the eve-ning on a Fri-day night. ____
See the pa-per lay-in' on the side-walk, ____ a lit-tle mu-sic from the house next door. ____

A lit-tle light a shin-in' through the win-dow ____
So I walk on up to the door-step, ____

Repeat and Fade

TAKE A CHANCE ON ME

Words and Music by BENNY ANDERSSON
and BJORN ULVAEUS

Moderate dance beat

TIE A YELLOW RIBBON
ROUND THE OLE OAK TREE

Words and Music by L. RUSSELL BROWN
and IRWIN LEVINE

TIME IN A BOTTLE

Words and Music by
JIM CROCE

WE ARE FAMILY

Words and Music by NILE RODGERS
and BERNARD EDWARDS

WHEN I NEED YOU

Words by CAROLE BAYER SAGER
Music by ALBERT HAMMOND

WHEN WILL I BE LOVED

Words and Music by
PHIL EVERLY

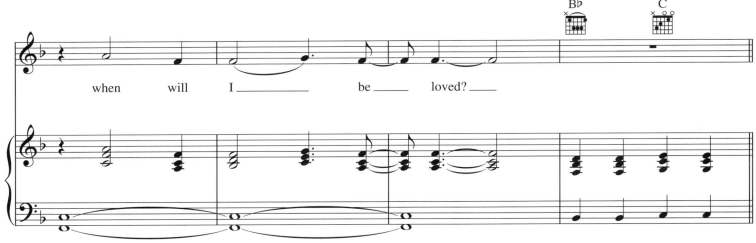

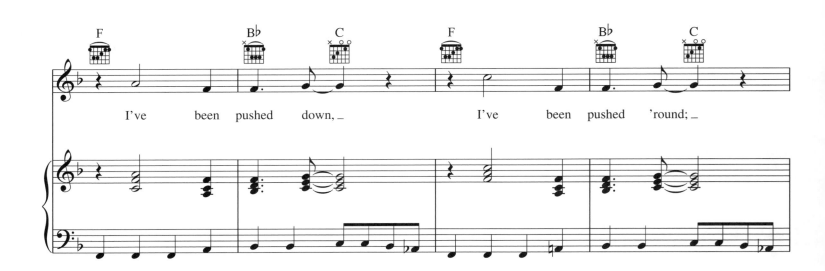

when will I _____ be ____ loved? ____

When I find my new man ____ that I want for

mine, he al - ways breaks _ my heart in two; ___ it

hap - pens ev - 'ry ____ time. _____

YOU'RE SO VAIN

Words and Music by
CARLY SIMON

YESTERDAY ONCE MORE

Words and Music by JOHN BETTIS
and RICHARD CARPENTER

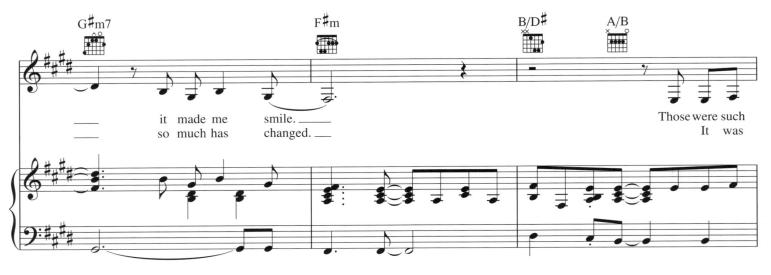

YOU LIGHT UP MY LIFE

Words and Music by
JOSEPH BROOKS

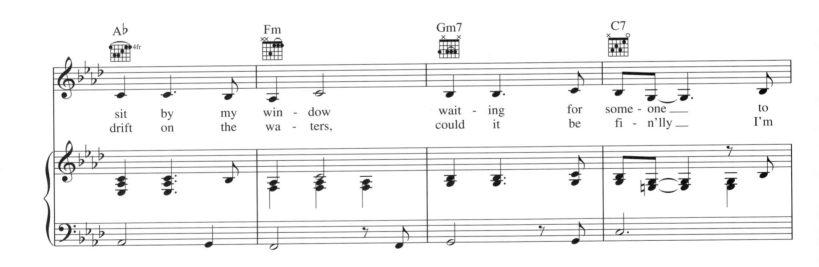

YOUR SONG

Words and Music by ELTON JOHN
and BERNIE TAUPIN

now that it's done, ___ I hope you don't mind, ___ I hope you don't mind ___ that I put ___ down in ___ words how won-der-ful life is ___ while you're ___ in ___ the world. ___

YOUR MAMA DON'T DANCE

Words and Music by JIM MESSINA
and KENNY LOGGINS

go to rock and roll? *Instrumental ends* You

pull in-to a drive-in and find a place to park. You hop in-to the back seat where you

know it's nice and dark. ___ You're just a-bout to move and you're

think-ing it's a breeze, ___ there's a light in your eye and then a guy ___ says,